Chicago

Chicago is one of the largest and busiest cities in the U.S. Almost three million people live and work in Chicago.

Chicago is on Lake Michigan. The Chicago River runs through the city. The city is an important shipping port and business center.

Chicago's O'Hare Airport is one of the busiest airports in the U.S.

Unit 1

Table of Contents

Grade 2

Texts for Close Reading

Table of Contents

Landfills

Every year, people throw away tons of trash. Finding a place for the trash is a big problem.

Garbage companies collect the garbage and dump it in landfills. Landfills are very big holes in the ground.

The existing landfills have too much trash. People do not want new landfills near their homes. People have to learn to throw away less. You can help by recycling your trash.

Plant Parts

Plants have parts that help keep the plant alive. The roots hold the plant in the ground. The roots also take in nutrients and water from the soil. The stem carries the water and nutrients to other parts of the plant. The leaves make food. The plant's flowers and fruit have seeds that can become new plants.

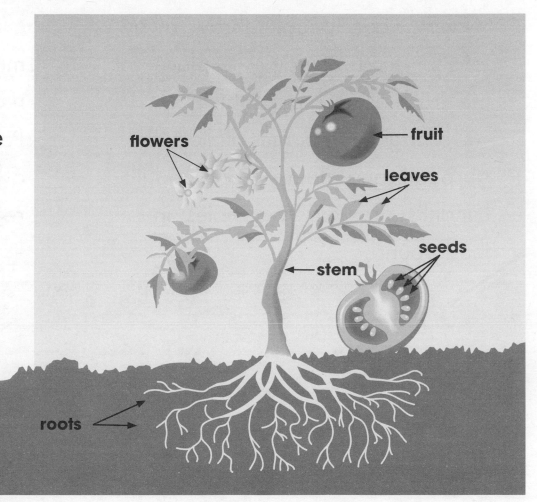

flowers

fruit

leaves

seeds

stem

roots

Bringing Back the Whooping Crane

by Jane Campbell and Susan Hartley

Table of Contents

Now You See Them . . .

Have you ever seen a whooping crane? Probably not! Only a few hundred of these rare birds are left. Sixty years ago, there were only about 20 whooping cranes. This book tells how people are working to bring back the whooping cranes.

Facts about Whooping Cranes

- They are found only in North America.
- They migrate from Canada to the southern United States.
- They are more than 5 feet tall.
- They are the tallest birds in North America.
- They have a **wingspan** of 7 feet.
- They get their name from the whooping cry they make.
- Their cry can be heard from 2 miles away.

8

Cranes in Danger

Before pioneers settled the North American prairies, there were thousands of whooping cranes. By the 1860s, there were only about 1,000 birds.

By 1940, only about 20 whooping cranes were left. What happened to make so many of these beautiful birds disappear?

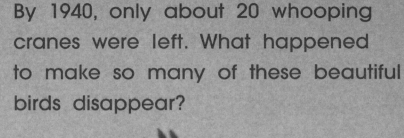

The cranes disappeared for three main reasons—loss of their **habitat**, overhunting, and egg collecting.

Loss of Habitat

Whooping cranes like to live in open, marshy places. In this habitat, they can find food and materials for shelter and nesting.

In the late 1800s and early 1900s, large areas of marshes were drained to create farmlands. This was a disaster for the whooping cranes.

Overhunting

Hunters shot whooping cranes as they **migrated** between Canada and the southern United States.

Egg Collecting

As the cranes became more rare, collectors took their eggs as souvenirs.

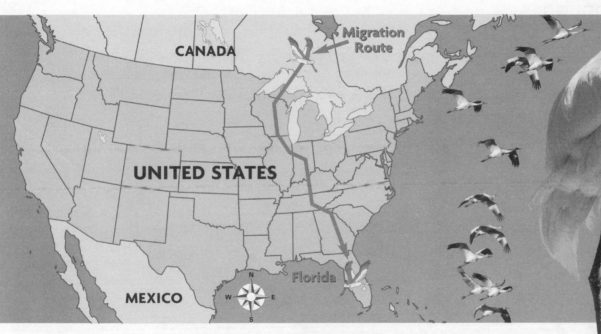

CANADA

Migration Route

UNITED STATES

MEXICO

Florida

the long route south for migrating whooping cranes

Cranes usually lay two eggs each season, but only one chick survives.

Saving the Whooping Crane

In 1970, the whooping crane was declared an **endangered species**. It became illegal to hunt the cranes or take their eggs. This helped, but it was not enough.

By the early 1980s, only one small flock of whooping cranes was left. To help bring back more cranes, the International Whooping Crane Recovery Team was formed.

People feared we might lose the last whooping crane flock to an oil spill.

These men are working to help whooping cranes.

Today, the wild whooping crane flock numbers nearly 200 birds. Two new whooping crane flocks are beginning to form. One of the new flocks lives year-round in central Florida.

Chicks are hatched in Maryland, Wisconsin, and Alberta, Canada.

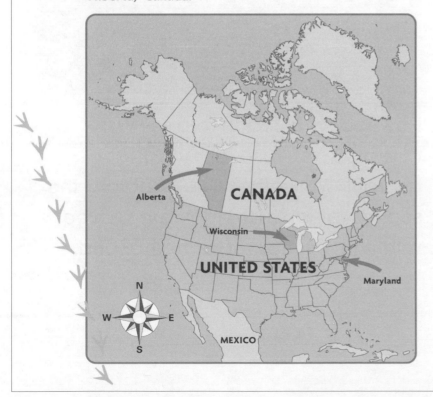

Chicks from the Florida flock are hatched and raised in captivity.

Later the chicks are released into the wild.

The recovery team wanted the second flock to migrate. This was a challenge. In the wild, chicks learn from their mothers how to migrate. But chicks hatched in **captivity** do not have mothers!

How do you teach cranes to migrate? You use an **ultralight** aircraft! While the chicks hatch, the sounds of an ultralight are played with the sounds of a mother bird.

When it is time to migrate south, the young birds follow the ultralight the same way they would follow a mother bird. In 2001, the first flock raised in captivity followed an ultralight aircraft from Wisconsin to Florida.

People who train the cranes wear protective clothing. They never talk to the birds.

The birds had to be shown the way only once! They were able to fly back on their own. Five of the birds made it back to Wisconsin in the spring.

An Incredible Recovery

Whooping cranes have made an incredible recovery! Their story shows how humans can help protect wildlife.

We should be alert to other animals whose habitats are in danger. We may be able to prevent them from disappearing, too.

Glossary

captivity	kept within bounds; birds in captivity are not free to fly where they want
endangered	in danger of disappearing
habitat	an area where plants, birds, or animals are able to live
migrate	to travel from one part of the world to another and back again every year
species	a group of animals, different from all other groups
ultralight	a type of small aircraft that does not weigh a lot
wingspan	the distance from the tip of one wing to the tip of the other

The Biggest Baseball Game of the Year

Announcer 1: Welcome to today's baseball game. The . . .

Announcer 2: Wow! Look at that! Penny Jones just hit a high fly to center field!

Announcer 1: The students of Hillcrest Elementary School are on one team, and their parents are on the other. The . . .

Announcer 2: Oops! Mr. Paul dropped the ball! Penny made it to first base.

Announcer 1: The players sold tickets to raise money for new books for the school . . .

Announcer 2: Another hit! The shortstop, Mrs. Monto, threw the ball to first base. Mr. Green caught the ball, and Mario Toon is out. Penny made it to second base, though.

Announcer 1: All the ticket money will go to the school library, where . . .

Announcer 2: Amazing! Billy Wiggins just hit a home run! The score is Students 2, Parents 0.

Announcer 1 and Announcer 2: This is going to be the biggest baseball game of the year!

Unit 2

Table of Contents

The Park Pond

Ting's mom was a gardener at the park. One Saturday, Ting went to help her mom. In the morning, they pulled weeds. Later they went to the pond and found it full of slime and trash.

"Use these gloves," said Ting's mom. "You can pick up the trash and put it in the bags. I will scoop the slime out of the water."

"Do the trash and slime make the frogs sick?" asked Ting.

"Yes, but they will be singing 'ribbit, ribbit' when the pond is clean again!

Little Duck

Little Duck wanted friends. Little Duck swam down the river. The ducks said, "Go away. You are ugly!"

Little Duck swam north to the forest. The animals said, "Go away. You are a funny-looking duck."

Little Duck was sad. Little Duck swam south to the lake. He saw some swans. "Swans are so pretty," said Little Duck.

Then Little Duck went to sleep. Little Duck slept for a long, long time.

Little Duck woke up and looked at himself in the lake.

"I do not believe what I am seeing," he said.

The swans saw Little Duck, too. The swans said, "You are not a duck. You are a pretty swan. We always knew you were beautiful."

Little Red Riding Hoodie Rides Again

Little Red Riding Hoodie had a basket of hot food. The food was for her sick grandmother. Little Red wanted to get to Granny's house before the food got cold. Little Red took a shortcut through the woods. A wolf stopped her.

"What's in your basket?" asked the wolf. Little Red knew better than to talk to strangers. Little Red kept walking.

The wolf tried again. He said, "I love your hoodie. Where did you get it?"

Little Red did not answer. She started to run. The wolf ran after her. Little Red ran out of the woods. The wolf followed her.

Luckily, the number 12 bus came by. Little Red got on the bus. The wolf did not have exact change.

The bus took Little Red to Granny's house. They ate happily ever after.

Why Spiders Have Small Waists

by Carol Pugliano-Martin • illustrated by Anita DuFalla

Once there was a spider named Anansi. He had a big round belly and he loved to eat. Anansi sang this song every day:

The problem was, Anansi didn't know when to stop eating. He ate and ate and ate. And when he was done, he always wanted more.

One day, while Anansi was eating, Elephant came by. "Anansi, have you heard? Lion is having a big feast. Come along."

Anansi beamed and sang his special song. And he began to follow Elephant to Lion's feast.

I love to eat! I love a treat! A great big feast can't be beat!

Then Monkey appeared.
"Anansi, have you heard?
Rhino is having a big feast.
Come along."

Anansi beamed and sang
his special song again.
And he began to follow Monkey
to Rhino's feast.

Then Anansi stopped short. "Wait a minute," he thought to himself.

"Which feast will begin first? If I go to one first and miss the other, I will miss lots of food! What should I do?"

Anansi had an idea. He called his two sons to him. "My sons, tie this string around my waist.

One of you take one end and wait at Lion's feast. The other take the other end and wait at Rhino's feast. When the feast is ready, pull on your end and I will go there first."

Anansi's sons did as they were told.
One son waited for Lion's feast
to begin.

The other son waited
for Rhino's feast to begin.

Meanwhile, Anansi beamed. "I am so clever. I will have double the food today."

Suddenly, Anansi felt a tug from one of the strings. "I'm ready to eat!" he shouted.

But then he felt another tug from the other side. Both feasts were beginning at the same time! The two sons tugged and tugged.

"Stop!" cried Anansi. But his sons could not hear him and they continued to tug. They tugged so hard that Anansi's waist became small.

That is why today spiders have small waists and cannot eat big meals.

Anansi was too greedy. He had learned his lesson.

Now Anansi sings a new song:

> I love to eat! I love a treat!
> But my greedy ways I can't repeat.

Tell the whole story of
Why Spiders Have Small Waists

Use these pictures as clues to help you remember the story. Use as many words from the story as you can.

Taking Care of Me

My body likes to be clean, so I wash with soap and water every day.

My body doesn't like cavities, so I try to brush and floss my teeth after every meal.

My body needs plenty of sleep—about ten hours each night—so I go to bed on time whenever I can.

My body needs food; foods that are good for me are best. I eat plenty of fruits, vegetables, bread, and meat. I drink plenty of milk, too.

My body needs exercise to stay healthy, fit, and strong. I stretch when I get up every morning, and I jog with my dad in the evening.

My body needs lots of liquids—mostly water. I drink extra water with my meals, on hot days, and when I exercise.

My body takes care of me; I take care of my body.

Unit 3

Table of Contents

Make an Animal Mask

You can make an animal mask. It's simple. Before you begin, choose what type of animal you want to become. Find a photograph or an illustration from a fiction book to help you visualize the animal. Then choose your paint and paper colors.

In addition to paint and paper, you will need a paper plate and a craft stick.

First, cover the paper plate with paint. Then, wait for the paint to dry. Use the colored paper to make ears and attach them to the paper plate. Draw your animal's face. Remember to look at the picture you found before you started. Finally, attach the craft stick to the paper plate. Now you have an animal mask!

Make a Compost Pile

Do you know how to turn garbage into riches? Make a compost pile. First, get grass clippings. Then get dead leaves and plants. Now put them in a pile outside. Over time the grass, leaves, and plants will turn into rich dirt.

Worms can help your compost pile. After eating grass, leaves, and plants, the worms leave behind good soil. New plants grow in the good soil.

You can put other things in the compost pile, too. Some people put in eggshells, fruit peels, and coffee grounds. After some time, the garbage turns into good, rich dirt.

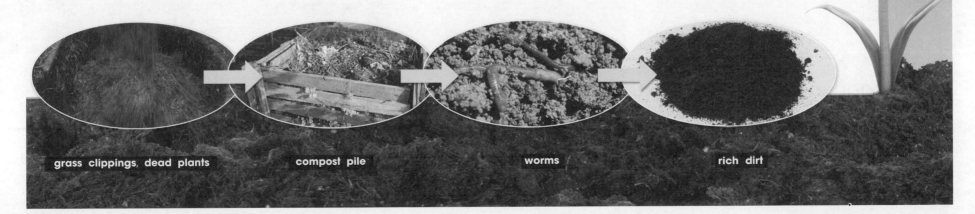

grass clippings, dead plants → compost pile → worms → rich dirt

The Bus Ride to Change

In 1955, a woman named Rosa Parks got on a bus and changed life for many Americans. After a long day of work, Rosa would not give up her seat on the bus. At the time, Ms. Parks was breaking a law. The bus driver called the police and Rosa Parks was arrested!

People were so angry about what happened to Rosa Parks that they stopped riding the buses. The Montgomery Bus Boycott began.

Finally in November 1956, the most powerful judges in the United States agreed that the bus law was not fair. The United States Supreme Court said people could sit anywhere they wanted to on the Montgomery buses. After the bus boycott, people worked hard to change other rules that were not fair.

An Oak Tree Has a Life Cycle

by Debra Castor

Table of Contents

Words to Think About

life cycle

An oak tree changes and grows during its life cycle.

seeds

Most plants begin as seeds.

plants

Many types of plants live on Earth.

stems

Stems bring water and nutrients to plants.

roots

Roots usually grow under the ground.

trunk

A tree has a trunk.

Introduction

All **plants** have a **life cycle**, or an order in which they change and grow.

During the life cycle, a plant grows the parts it needs to stay alive and to make new plants.

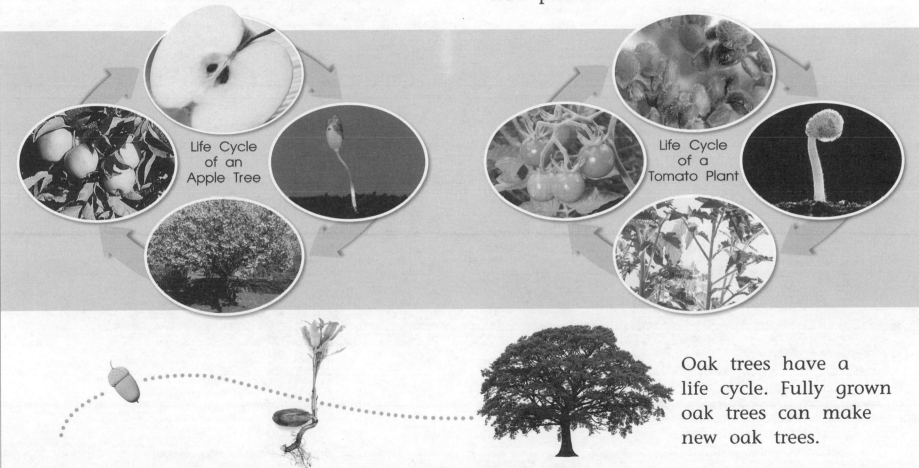

Life Cycle of an Apple Tree

Life Cycle of a Tomato Plant

Oak trees have a life cycle. Fully grown oak trees can make new oak trees.

A New Oak Tree Begins

At first, a fully grown oak tree drops **seeds**. These seeds are acorns.

Animals will eat most of the acorns, but a few acorns will become new oak trees.

▲ This acorn fell from an oak tree.

▲ This squirrel found an acorn on the ground.

Chapter 2

A New Oak Tree Grows

A few months after the acorn falls, **roots** begin to grow. The roots grow into the ground.

Next, a **stem** grows from the acorn. Leaves grow from the stem during the first year. Now the oak tree is a sapling.

roots

leaves

stem

Plant Fact

An oak tree is a seedling before it is a sapling.

▲ Roots grow if the acorn stays moist and cool.

▲ This sapling has just a few leaves.

Unit 3

Unit 3

Slowly, the oak tree becomes larger. At last, the stem becomes a thick, strong **trunk**.

Flowers grow on the oak tree and then the flowers become acorns. What will happen to these acorns?

oak tree flower

trunk

stem

acorns

LOOK AT TEXT STRUCTURE

Sequence of Events

This book shows a sequence, or order, of events. Find the words "at last." These words help you understand the sequence. What other words in this book help you understand the sequence?

An Old Oak Tree Dies

After dropping acorns for many years, the oak tree finally dies. An oak tree can live for hundreds of years.

Can you see oak trees where you live?

▲ Finally, the oak tree dies.

▲ This oak tree is about 1,500 years old.

▲ This new oak tree grows in a forest.

Conclusion

An oak tree is a plant that changes and grows. An oak tree has a life cycle.

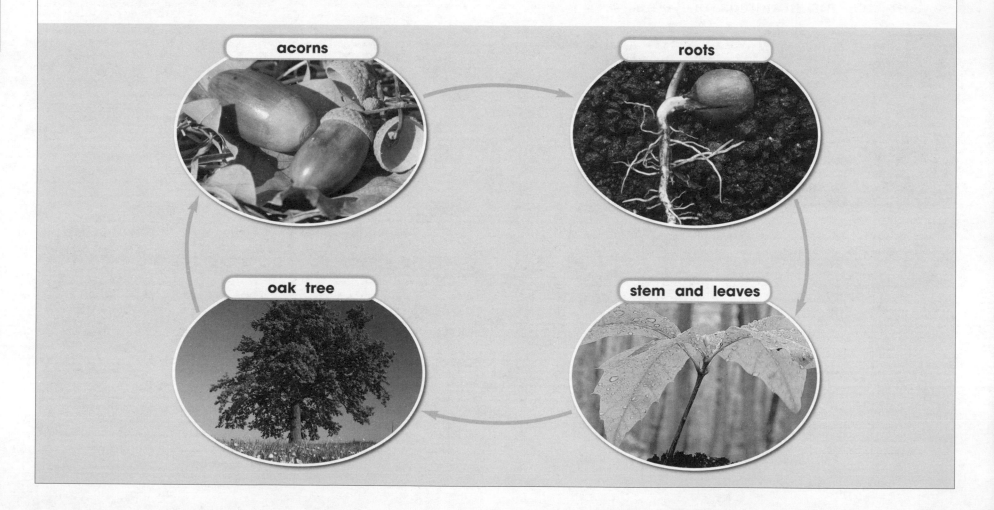

acorns

roots

oak tree

stem and leaves

Glossary

life cycle the order of how a living thing changes as it grows

plants living things that make their own food and stay in one place as they grow

roots parts of plants that are usually under the ground

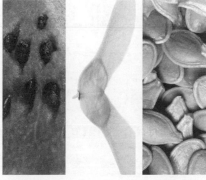

seeds parts of plants that grow into new plants

stems parts of plants that carry water and nutrients

trunk the stem of a grown tree

School Riddles

Question: An animal flies around the school at night. What is it?

Answer: The alpha-bat!

Question: The teacher wrote a math assignment. Why did he write it on the window?

Answer: He wanted to make sure it was very clear!

Question: Some elementary schools have class pets. Why don't you ever see giraffes?

Answer: They're all in high school!

Question: A boy in my class had a dictionary in his pocket. What did everyone call him?

Answer: Smarty pants!

Question: We all have friends at school. Who is everyone's best friend?

Answer: The princi-pal!

Unit 4

Table of Contents

The Lost Color

The Crayon Man made crayons in every color. He worked in his crayon factory day and night.

One day, the Crayon Man walked through his factory. Something was odd. He saw red, yellow, blue, orange, and purple crayons. But there were no green crayons!

"Oh, dear. We have lost our green!" the Crayon Man cried. "What will we do? How will children draw grass, frogs, and big green monsters?"

He thought and thought. Then the Crayon Man had an idea. He went into his lab and mixed the blue crayon potion with the yellow crayon potion.

A big smile grew on the Crayon Man's face. "We have green crayons again!"

A Frog Someday

My big brother can catch a fly on his tongue and eat it!

My big brother always has fun.

I am just a tadpole. I can't eat flies. I do not have a tongue.

My brother can hop on land. I cannot leave the water. I do not have legs yet.

"I have no fun!" I told my brother.

"You were an egg. Now you are a tadpole. One day you will be a frog, like me," said my brother.

Lost Dog

One day, Erica came home from school to find that her dog, Zak, was not at home. Zak had made a hole under the fence and had run away. Erica and her dad looked everywhere for Zak. They walked all around the neighborhood. They looked high and low.

"We are lost, too!" said Erica's dad. Then Erica saw Zak!

"It's OK, Dad," said Erica. "Zak will show us the way home. Look, he's sniffing his way back home right now!"

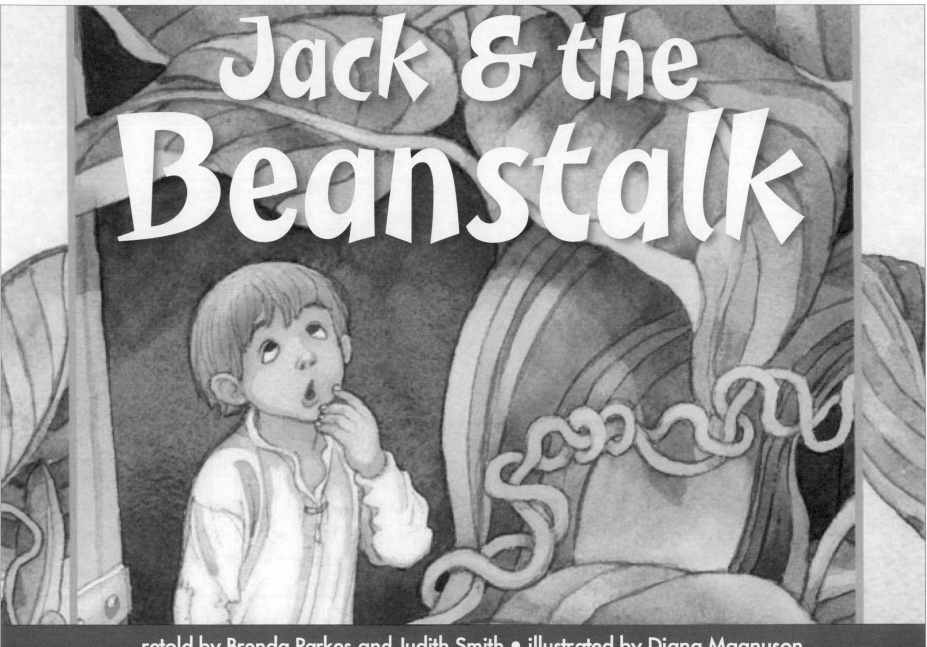

Jack & the Beanstalk

retold by Brenda Parkes and Judith Smith • illustrated by Diana Magnuson

Long ago, there lived a poor widow
and her son, Jack.
All they owned was a cow.
Every day they sold some of the cow's milk.
Then, one morning, the cow
stopped giving milk.

Jack's mother said to him,
"Take the cow to the market.
Sell her and bring me the money."

On the way to the market,
Jack met an old woman.
"Do you want to sell your cow?"
she asked him.
"Yes," said Jack.

Then the old woman said to Jack,
"Give me your cow,
and I'll give you these beans."
"I don't want beans," said Jack.
"But these beans are **magic,**"
said the old woman.
So Jack took the beans
and he gave the cow to the
old woman.

When Jack got home his mother said,
"Where's the money?"
"I haven't got any money," replied Jack.
"I've got **magic beans.**"
"**Magic beans!**" said his mother.
"**No** money! **No** cow! Only **beans!**"
And she threw the beans away.

His mother was very **very** angry
and Jack was very **very** sad.
He went to bed.

When Jack woke up next morning,
the room was dark.
Through the window he could see
a **huge** stalk and **huge** leaves.

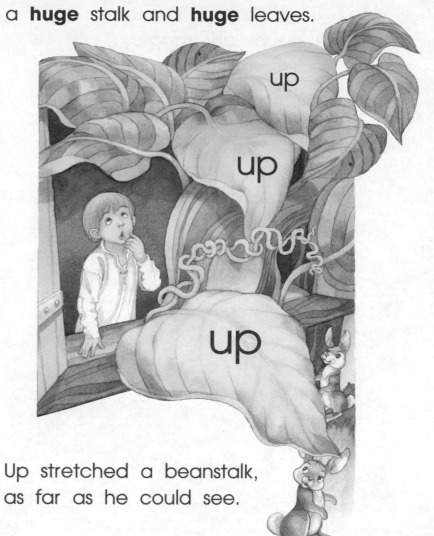

up

up

up

Up stretched a beanstalk,
as far as he could see.

Jack climbed out of the window and he climbed up the stalk.

He climbed and he climbed.
He could see his house far below.

Up he climbed through the clouds.
Then he reached a road.
He could see a beautiful castle.
It towered up into the sky.

Jack felt very scared.
But he thought to himself,
"I'm going to find out who lives here."
He walked right up to the castle
and he knocked on the castle door.

The door swung open.
The old woman stood there,
staring at Jack.
"What are you doing here?" she said.
"A wicked **Ogre** lives in this castle
and he doesn't like little boys."
"But I'm hungry," said Jack.

So the old woman took Jack
into the kitchen. "Sit down," she said,
"and I'll give you something to eat."
But suddenly the floor began to shake!

BANG   BANG   BANG

"It's the **Ogre!**" said the old woman.
"Quick! Get into the oven."
Jack got into the oven just in time.
The door flew open,
and in strode a **GIGANTIC** Ogre.

The **Ogre** shouted,
Fee-fi-fo-fum,
I smell the blood
of an Englishman.
If he's alive, or if he's dead,
I'll grind his bones
to make my bread.

"There's no one here, except me,"
said the old woman.
So the **Ogre** sat down at the table
and the woman gave him some food.
Jack lay **very very** still in the oven.
He was **very very** frightened.

When the **Ogre** had eaten his food,
he took out a big bag of gold.
"Look," he said to the old woman.
"I got lots of gold for that boy's cow."
The **Ogre** sat and counted the gold.
And then at last he went to sleep.

Jack looked at the **Ogre**
and he looked at the gold.
"That's my gold," he thought.
"The **Ogre** sold my cow."
So Jack crept out of the oven
and he grabbed the bag of gold.

Jack ran to the castle door.
He pushed the door,
but it wouldn't open!
He pushed again.
Then suddenly, the door opened
with a loud screech!

Jack ran out of the door
and down the road.

Behind him he could hear,
Fee-fi-fo-fum,
I smell the blood
of an Englishman.
If he's alive, or if he's dead,
I'll grind his bones
to make my bread.

It was the **Ogre**!
Jack ran faster and faster.
Behind him he could hear,

**Fee-fi-fo-fum,
I smell the blood
of an Englishman.
If he's alive, or if he's dead,
I'll grind his bones
to make my bread.**

The **Ogre** was chasing him.
Poor Jack!

Clutching the bag of gold,
Jack climbed back on to the beanstalk.
He started to climb down,
down through the clouds.

down

down

down

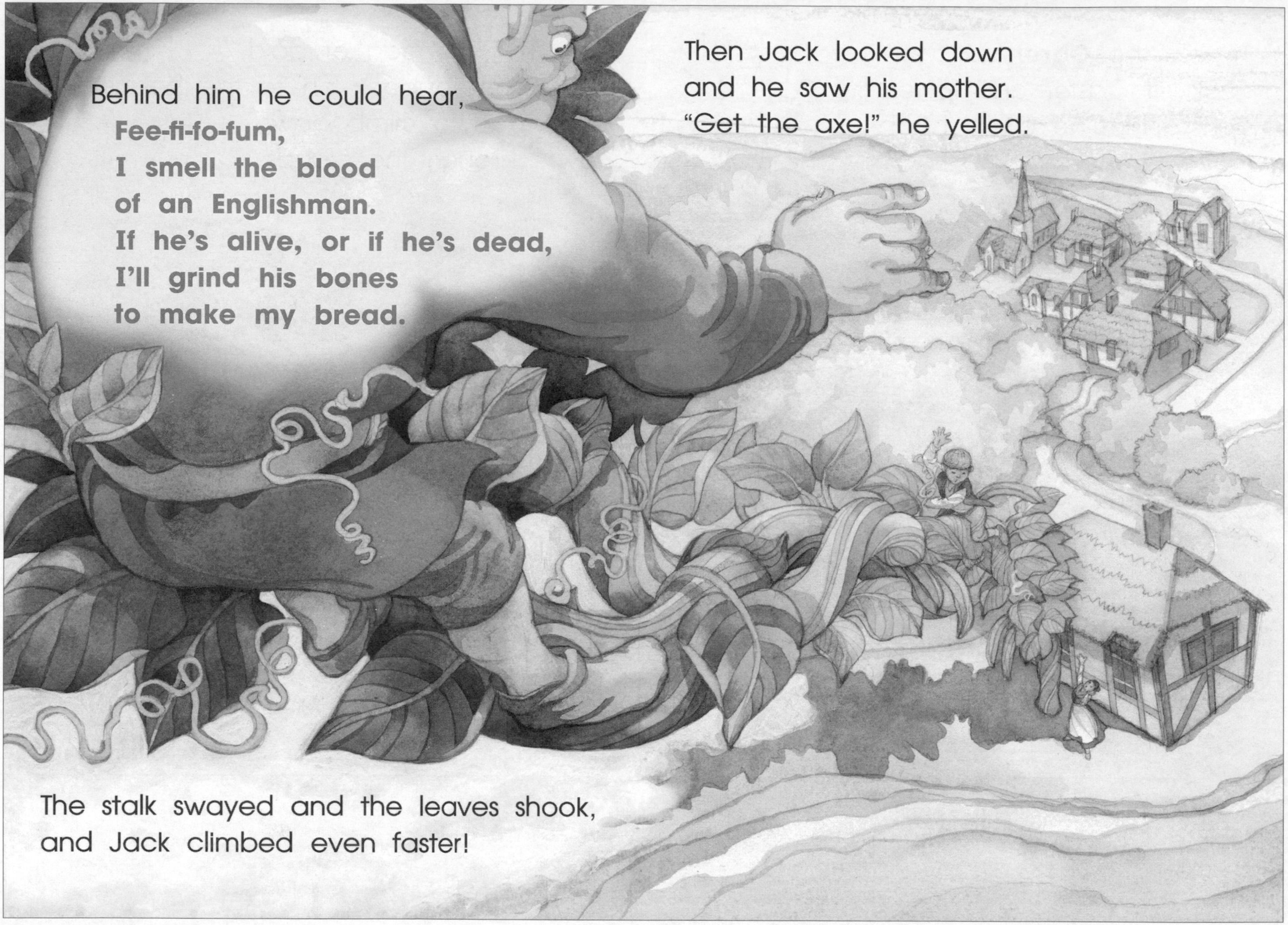

Behind him he could hear,
Fee-fi-fo-fum,
I smell the blood
of an Englishman.
If he's alive, or if he's dead,
I'll grind his bones
to make my bread.

Then Jack looked down
and he saw his mother.
"Get the axe!" he yelled.

The stalk swayed and the leaves shook,
and Jack climbed even faster!

As Jack reached the ground,
his mother chopped
through the beanstalk.
And that was the end of the **Ogre!**
Jack and his mother were safe
and they lived happily ever after.

What happened in the story?

Interviewing Granddad

Kids: Granddad, what did you like to do when you were our age?

Granddad: I mostly liked to play with my friends. I still do, too.

Kids: What did you like to read when you were our age?

Granddad: I mostly liked to read adventure books. I still do, too.

Kids: What did you like to eat when you were our age?

Granddad: I mostly liked to eat chocolate chip cookies. I still do, too.

Kids: We thought you were old, Granddad. But instead, you're just like us!

Granddad: I guess I am. Who wants a cookie?

Unit 5

Table of Contents

What's the Rush?

The alarm went off. Lucy looked at the clock to see what time it was. A look of horror showed on her face.

Then she heard the honking outside. Quickly she put on her raincoat and grabbed her umbrella. She slid her feet into her boots.

Rushing to the door, Lucy picked up a stack of books from the table. With her arms full, she hurried out.

Grouping Living Things

We can group all things into living and nonliving things. We can group living things into animals and plants. Animals must find food to eat. Plants make their own food. Most animals move as they grow. Most plants stay in one place as they grow.

We can group animals by how they look. Some animals have backbones. Other animals do not have backbones. Insects, spiders, and snails do not have backbones. Five types of animals have backbones, including fish, amphibians, reptiles, mammals, and birds.

Coral Reefs

A coral reef is a type of habitat. Coral reefs grow best near land in clean, warm water.

A coral polyp is a small animal that lives in the water. A hard skeleton forms around the coral polyp's body. The skeleton protects the coral polyp. The skeleton stays when the coral polyp dies. More coral polyps attach to the skeleton. The coral reef grows.

An octopus can live on a coral reef. A puffer and a stingray can live on a coral reef, too.

A coral reef is also home to algae, a type of plant. Algae make food for coral polyps. Sea grass lives on coral reefs, too. Many animals use sea grass for food and shelter.

Life in an Urban Community
by Margaret McNamara

Table of Contents

Words to Think About

apartments

These buildings have many apartments.

city

This city is an urban community.

community helpers

These community helpers keep the city safe and clean.

homes

Urban communities have many types of homes.

jobs

People have jobs to earn money.

urban community

An urban community is the largest type of community.

Introduction

A community is a place where people live, work, and play. An **urban community** is the largest type of community.

Big **cities** are urban communities. Many people live in big cities. The people live closer together than in other kinds of communities.

▲ This city is an urban community.

Other Types of Communities

suburban community

rural community

Unit 5

Homes

An urban community has **homes**. Often the homes are close together because so many people live in the community.

Some families live in **apartments**. Many apartments are in one building.

apartments

LOOK AT TEXT STRUCTURE

Cause and Effect

Find the word "because." The author uses this word to show a cause-and-effect relationship. The reason, or cause, is that many people live in the community. What is the effect?

▲ People live in these homes.

Jobs

In an urban community, many people work for large companies. They work in office buildings.

Some people walk to their **jobs**. Other people take buses, taxis, or subways. Some people drive to work.

taxi

subway

Going Green

Many large cities have public transportation, such as buses and trains. People help Earth by using public transportation.

Unit 5

Every city has **community helpers**. Community helpers keep the city safe and clean.

Other workers help people, too. They provide the services people need.

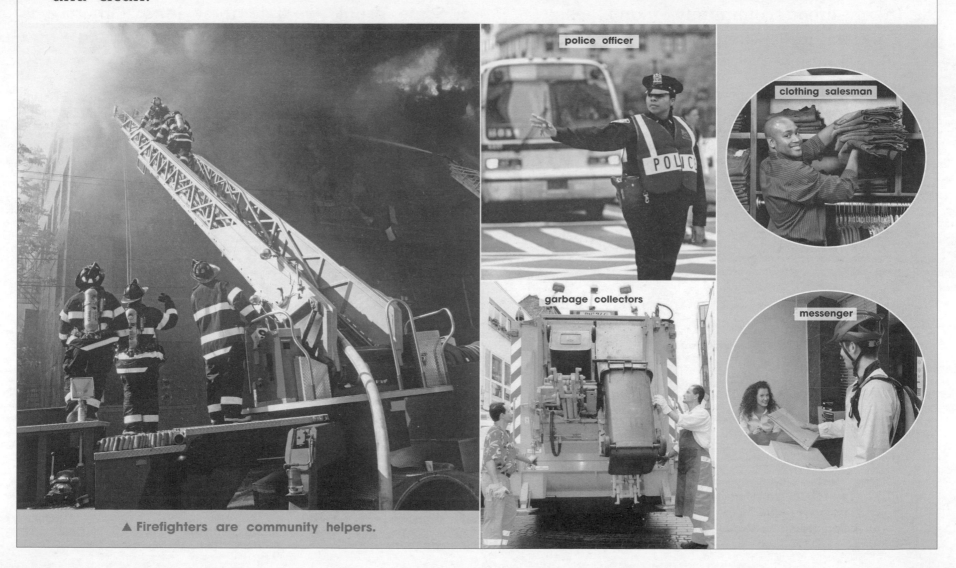

▲ Firefighters are community helpers.

police officer

clothing salesman

garbage collectors

messenger

76

Unit 5

Places to Play and Explore

Urban communities can be crowded, but people still find places to play. Most cities have parks where people can go.

Cities build playgrounds, too. They also have many places to explore.

▲ Museums are great places to explore and learn.

Unit 5

Conclusion

Many people live in cities. Cities are urban communities.

Urban communities are the largest type of community.

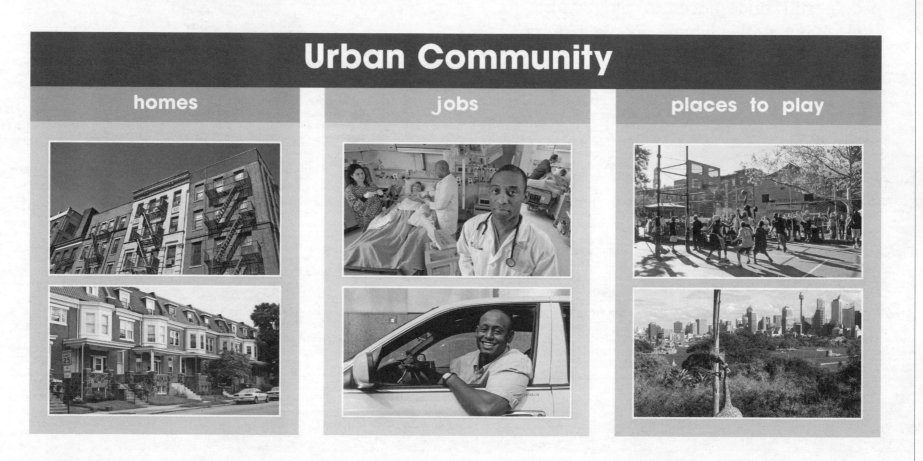

Urban Community

| homes | jobs | places to play |

Glossary

apartments homes inside a larger building

city a very large community

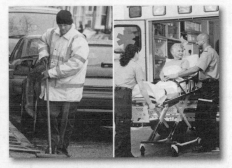

community helpers people who have jobs that help the community

homes places where people live

jobs types of work that people do

urban community a large community where people live, work, and play

Unit 5

Maggie's Story

"We will write stories," said the teacher, Mrs. Day. "Here's some paper. Please draw a picture, too."

"I can't think of anything to write," Maggie whispered to Mrs. Day.

"Keep thinking!" Mrs. Day whispered back.

"May I write a cooking story?" asked Andy. "My mom and I made up a new recipe!"

"Good thinking," said Mrs. Day.

"May I write a running story?" asked Zoe. "My track club ran at the rec center after school yesterday!"

"Good thinking," said Mrs. Day.

"May I write about my messy room?" asked Willy. "I haven't seen the floor in WEEKS!"

"Good thinking," said Mrs. Day.

"I still can't think of anything to write," Maggie whispered to Mrs. Day.

"You could write a story about not having anything to write," Mrs. Day whispered back.

"GOOD THINKING!" said Maggie.

Unit 6

Table of Contents

Ma's Runaway Pumpkin

Ma wanted to make a pumpkin pie for Thanksgiving. She went to the garden. Ma picked a pumpkin and it began to roll away. "Stop!" Ma cried.

The pumpkin rolled out of the garden. Ma ran after it. The pumpkin rolled across the field and down the hill.

Finally, it rolled into a tree. Bam! The pumpkin broke into pieces. Some mice saw the broken pumpkin. "Dinner!" said the mice.

Ma looked and looked for the runaway pumpkin. Finally, she saw it.

"There you are!" she said.

The mice looked at Ma. Ma ran toward the mice. They were too full to run away. Then Ma smiled. "Happy Thanksgiving!" Ma said.

Neighborhoods

Neighborhoods are places where people live, work, play, and go to school. All kinds of people live in neighborhoods. People bring their special skills and cultural backgrounds to the neighborhood.

People's special skills help make life easier. A variety of cultural backgrounds makes a neighborhood interesting and enjoyable. You can see and experience different cultures in neighborhood stores, restaurants, and festivals.

Unit 6

In a Tropical Rain Forest

Many animals live in a tropical rain forest. Some insects have nests on the forest floor. Other animals move between the forest floor and the understory, or second layer of the rain forest. Still other animals live mostly in the understory.

Most animals are in the canopy, or third layer of the rain forest. The animals there range from butterflies and bats to large animals like sloths.

Finally, the emergent, or top, layer of the rain forest is home to many birds. The birds have nests in the high branches.

Unit 6

Postcard Clues

by Linda Johns • illustrated by Anita DuFalla

My name is Sarah. I live in St. Louis, Missouri. My mom and I are going on a long trip. I say good-bye to my best friend Sam.

Sam says, "Have fun on your trip. Send me a postcard."

I tell her, "I'll send you a postcard from every place Mom and I visit. I'll put clues on the postcards. You can use the clues to guess what we're seeing or where we are."

Dear Sam,

Greetings from the west coast of the United States. Today I visited the second longest suspension bridge in the country! It was kind of scary to be so high up over San Francisco Bay, but the view of the Pacific Ocean was really cool.
Can you guess which bridge we saw?

Your friend,
Sarah

5 Longest Suspension Bridges in the United States

Verrazano-Narrows, New York	4,260	feet
Golden Gate, California	4,200	feet
Mackinac, Michigan	3,800	feet
George Washington, New York	3,500	feet
Second Tacoma, Washington	2,800	feet

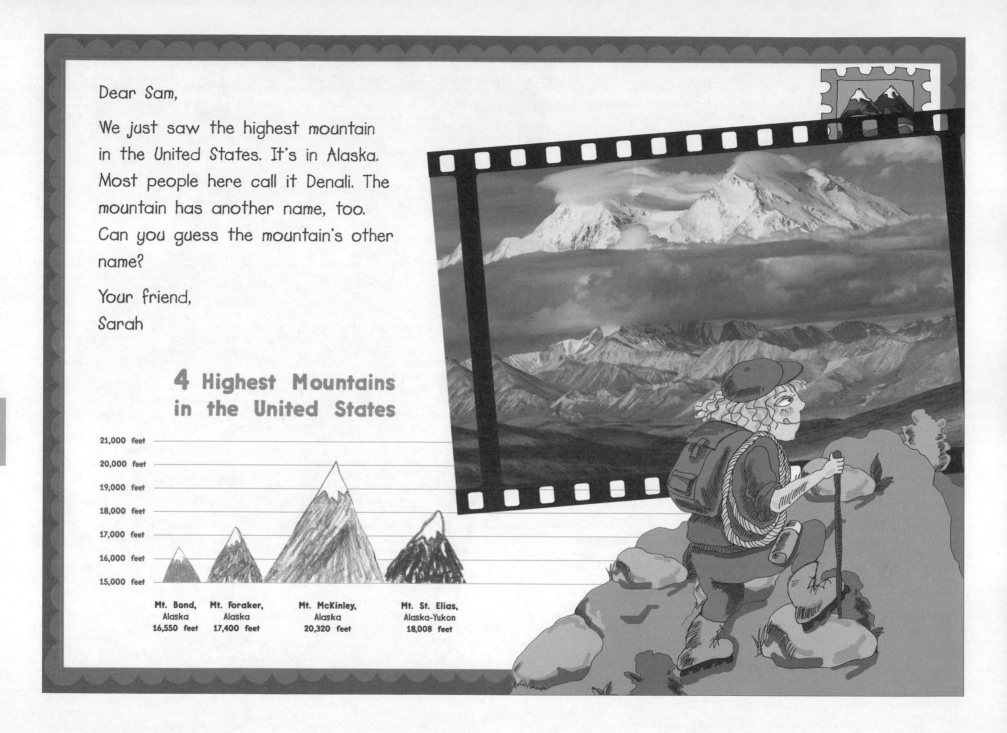

Dear Sam,

We just saw the highest mountain in the United States. It's in Alaska. Most people here call it Denali. The mountain has another name, too. Can you guess the mountain's other name?

Your friend,
Sarah

4 Highest Mountains in the United States

21,000 feet			
20,000 feet			
19,000 feet			
18,000 feet			
17,000 feet			
16,000 feet			
15,000 feet			

Mt. Bond, Alaska 16,550 feet

Mt. Foraker, Alaska 17,400 feet

Mt. McKinley, Alaska 20,320 feet

Mt. St. Elias, Alaska-Yukon 18,008 feet

88

Dear Sam,

Greetings from "down under"! That's what they call Australia.

We went scuba diving and saw the most beautiful fish and plants. They live in more than 1,000 miles of coral off the northeast coast of Australia. Can you guess where we went scuba diving?

Your friend,
Sarah

Australia

INDIAN OCEAN

Great Barrier Reef

PACIFIC OCEAN

Uluru (Ayres Rock)

Sydney

Canberra

N W E S

PACIFIC OCEAN

Unit 6

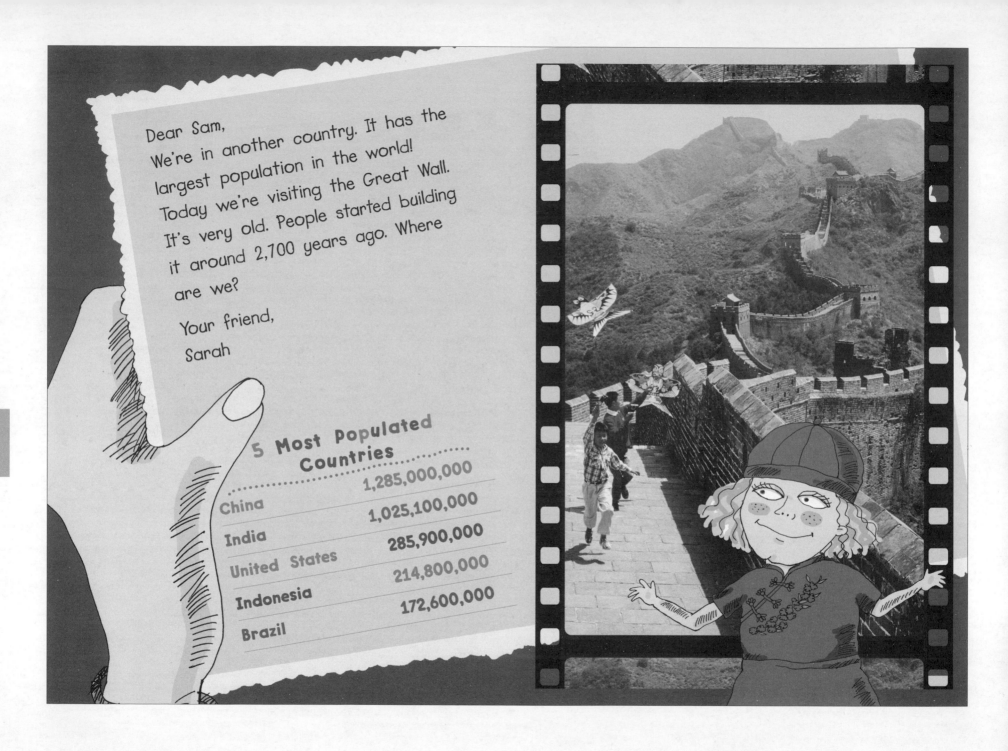

Dear Sam,
We're in another country. It has the largest population in the world! Today we're visiting the Great Wall. It's very old. People started building it around 2,700 years ago. Where are we?

Your friend,
Sarah

5 Most Populated Countries

China	1,285,000,000
India	1,025,100,000
United States	285,900,000
Indonesia	214,800,000
Brazil	172,600,000

Dear Sam,

We are at a huge lake. It's so big that it's called a sea. In fact, it's the largest lake in the world. It borders countries in Europe and Asia. What lake are we visiting?

Your friend,
Sarah

4 Largest Lakes in the World

Lakes	Size in Square Miles
Caspian Sea	143,240
Lake Superior	31,700
Lake Victoria	26,820
Lake Huron	23,000

Unit 6

Dear Sam,

Buon giorno! That's the way we say "good day" here in Italy. Today we're visiting a volcano near the city of Naples. The ancient city of Pompeii was buried when this volcano erupted more than 2,000 years ago.

Can you guess what volcano it is?

Your friend,
Sarah

Italy

ADRIATIC SEA

Naples
Vesuvius

MEDITERRANEAN SEA

N
W E
S

92

Dear Sam,

Now we're visiting a province in eastern Canada. This province is a peninsula. The name of this province means New Scotland. We're having fun sailing around the Bay of Fundy and whale watching. What province are we visiting?

Your friend,
Sarah

CANADA

QUEBEC

Newfoundland and Labrador

P.E.I.

NEW BRUNSWICK

NOVA SCOTIA

Bay of Fundy

U.S.A.

ATLANTIC OCEAN

Eastern Canada
Nova Scotia
New Brunswick
P.E.I. (Prince Edward Island)
Newfoundland and Labrador
U.S.A.

Unit 6

Dear Sam,

This is your last postcard!
I'm in a city in the United States.
The latitude is about 38 degrees.
The longitude is about 90 degrees.
Come find me! I'll be waiting.

Your friend,
Sarah

the United States

Unit 7

Table of Contents

The Perfect Pet

Polly wanted a pet. Most pets made her sneeze. But Polly was sure she could find the perfect pet.

At the pet store, Polly looked at the fluffy puppies. "They're so cute! I want a . . . a . . . achoo! Not a puppy," Polly said sadly.

Then she saw the soft, furry kittens. "Oh, I want a . . . a . . . achoo! No, not a kitten either," she said.

Next, Polly saw a pet with no hair or fur. It had a hard shell with a pretty pattern. "I want a . . . turtle!" And she did not sneeze.

Which pet do you predict Polly brought home?

What Will Henry Do?

Henry is a responsible boy. His mother gave him money to buy a healthful lunch. Some students are selling chocolate to raise money for their soccer team. Henry wants to buy the chocolate, but if he does, he won't have enough money to buy lunch. Henry knows that his body needs healthful foods. What will Henry do with his money?

Unit 7

Germs

Bacteria are very tiny living things. Some bacteria cause disease. Disease-causing bacteria are germs.

Germs can get into our bodies in different ways. When someone sneezes or coughs on you, germs get into your body. Germs can get in through cuts or food, too.

What might happen if we eat food with germs on it?

THE UGLY DUCKLING

retold by Brenda Parkes and Judith Smith • illustrated by Jacqueline Rogers

Once upon a time,
a duck sat on a nest of eggs.
Day after day she sat and sat.
Until
the eggs began to crack.
Out came five little ducklings.
They were fluffy and yellow!

One egg was left in the nest.
Then that egg cracked, too.
Out popped a big gray duckling.
"Who are **you**?" said the mother duck.
"Go away! Go away! You're **ugly**,"
chirped the five yellow ducklings.

Unit 7

Every day, the ugly duckling
grew bigger and BIGGER,
and uglier and UGLIER.

The other ducks came to look at him.
"You **are** ugly," they said.

The ugly duckling grew very sad.
"No one wants me," he said
as he swam in the river.
The other ducklings teased him.
The big ducks pecked at him.

And the ugly duckling grew
sadder and SADDER.

©2014 Benchmark Education Company, LLC

Unit 7

"No one wants me,"
thought the ugly duckling.
"I'm going to run away."
So he swam sadly off down the river.

After a long time,
he met some wild ducks.
They looked at him and said,
"My! You **are** ugly!"

Then the wild
ducks flew away.
They left the ugly
duckling all alone.

Each day the winds grew colder.
The leaves fell off the trees,
and then it started to snow.

Then the river turned to ice.
It was winter.

The poor ugly duckling swam alone
in the river.

The duckling hid among the reeds.
He was cold and hungry,
and he was all alone.

After a long time, the ice began to melt.

The trees put on leaves.
The sun shone.
The sky was blue.
And the birds began to sing.

Slowly the duckling ruffled his feathers.
He walked down to the river.
He slid into the water
and he began to swim.

Then he looked down at the water.
To his amazement, he saw
a **beautiful** bird with a long, long neck.
"Who is that?" asked the ugly duckling.

Suddenly he heard a flapping of wings.
He looked up and he saw other birds.
They were like the bird in the water,
and they were beautiful, too.

The beautiful birds landed in the water.
They swam around the duckling
and they began to stroke him.
"Who are you?" asked the ugly duckling.
"We're swans like you," they replied.

"But I am an **ugly** duckling," he said.
"Look at yourself," said the swans.
And the duckling looked,
         and he looked.

The ugly duckling was **not**
an ugly duckling any more.
He was a beautiful swan.
"I'm a swan like you," he said.
"I've found my very own family!"

And he lived happily ever after!

What happened in the story?

Unit 7

The Candy Jar

Group 1: We came home. We found it here.

Group 2: This must be it.

Group 1: You must be right.

Group 2: Take a little. Only a little.

Group 1: That's very good.

Group 2: Kind of nice.

Group 1: I need more. Hand it over.

Group 2: Think before you act!

Group 1: I need help. I don't feel well.

Group 2: I know why!

Group 1: Same time tomorrow?

Group 2: Same time tomorrow!

Group 1 and Group 2: Home, sweet home!

Unit 8

Table of Contents

Measure It!

Rulers and scales are tools. These tools are alike in several ways. We can use both tools to measure objects. We use both tools in our homes, schools, and offices.

Rulers and scales are different in some ways, too. We use a ruler to see how long an object is. We can measure length in inches or centimeters. A scale, on the other hand, determines how heavy an object is. We can measure weight in ounces and pounds, or grams and kilograms.

Amazing Storms

A thunderstorm starts with a dark cloud and brings rain or ice, wind, lightning, and thunder.

Many thunderstorms last for about an hour.

A hurricane starts over the ocean. Like in a thunderstorm, rain falls and powerful winds blow. Big waves wash onto the land. Some hurricanes last a whole week!

A tornado has rain and winds that twist quickly and pick up dirt and dust. The tall, dark cloud tears across the land. Tornadoes are shorter than thunderstorms and hurricanes. Some tornadoes last only a few minutes.

Unit 8

Trees

All trees have some of the same parts. All trees have roots that grow in the ground. The roots keep the tree in place. Trees also have trunks. The trunk has bark on the outside to protect the tree. Trees have branches, too.

Different trees have different kinds of branches. Some trees have thick branches, while others have thin branches. Some trees have branches that point up, while others have branches that spread out.

Unit 8

Transportation Past and Present

by Matthew Frank

Table of Contents

Unit 8

Words to Think About

future

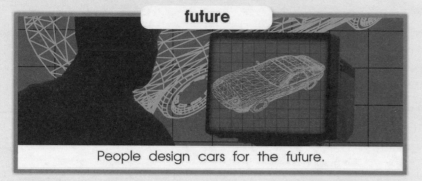

People design cars for the future.

past

These cars are from the past.

goods

People buy and sell goods.

present

This car is from the present.

inventors

Henry Ford   Garrett Morgan   the Wright Brothers

transportation

People use transportation to get places.

Unit 8

Introduction

What is **transportation**? Transportation is how people and things move from place to place.

We can look at how transportation has changed over time. We can compare the **past** and the **present**.

boat

train

solar-powered car

jet airplane

Unit 8

Waterways

In the past, people who lived near water used rafts and small boats to carry things. Later, steamboats were used to transport **goods** and people.

We use ships today, too. Now many ships can move faster than before. They can carry more goods and people, too.

▲ The *Clermont* carried people, cotton, and soap.

▲ People still transport goods on the water.

Viking longboat

raft

hovercraft

cruise ship

Railways

Long ago, people used horses and wagons as transportation. Then **inventors** made trains.

Today people still use trains. However, today's trains move faster because railroad tracks are better.

▲ Steam engine trains were faster than horses and wagons.

cable car

diesel-electric train

LOOK AT TEXT STRUCTURE

Compare and Contrast
The author uses the word "however" to compare trains in the present with trains long ago.

▲ This train carries things people need.

maglev train

subway

Unit 8

Roadways

The Model T was the first car many people could buy. It could go only about 45 miles per hour. People drove on cobblestone and dirt roads.

Today people drive many types of cars. These cars go much faster than cars in the past. Most people drive their cars on paved roads.

▲ These Model T cars are on a cobblestone road.

Helpful History

Garrett Morgan was an inventor. We have traffic signals today because of the work Mr. Morgan did in the past.

▲ An interstate highway is a long, paved roadway.

chariot

truck

car

truck

Unit 8

Chapter 4

Airways

The first airplane flight, in 1903, lasted 12 seconds. The airplane traveled a little farther than the length of a basketball court.

Today some flights last more than 15 hours! Many airplanes travel 600 miles per hour, and people can go almost anywhere on Earth.

▲ The Wright brothers flew the first airplane.

▲ Today many people travel on jets.

Leonardo da Vinci helicopter

hot air balloon

helicopter

shuttle

Unit 8

Conclusion

People use transportation to move from place to place. How has transportation changed over time?

How might transportation change in the **future**?

Past	Present

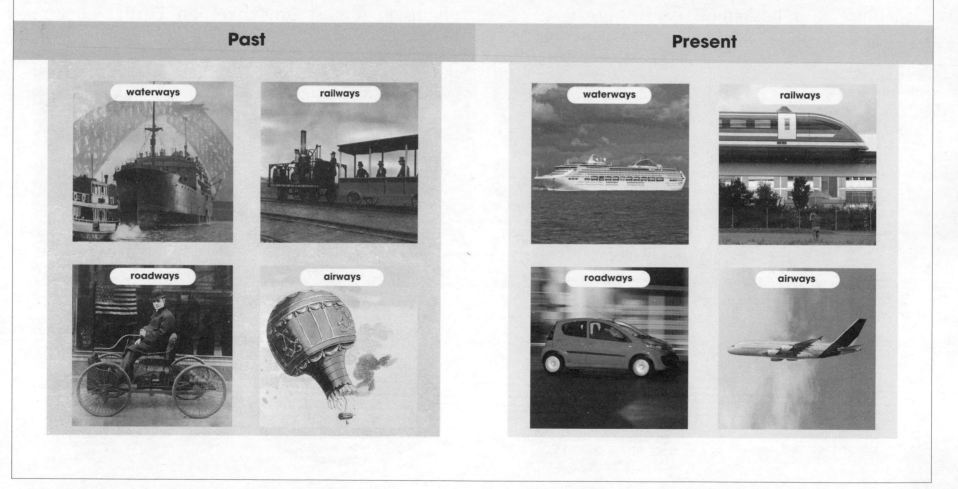

waterways · railways · roadways · airways

waterways · railways · roadways · airways

Unit 8

Glossary

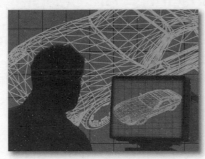

future time that has not happened yet

goods things people buy and sell

inventor the first person to make something

past time that has already happened

present time that is happening now

transportation how people and goods move from place to place

Unit 8

Now THAT'S a Pumpkin!

A "huge" contest happens every fall in Half Moon Bay, California. Farmers bring pumpkins from all over for the World Championship Pumpkin Weigh-Off. Winning pumpkins win prizes and money.

The first Weigh-Off was in 1974. The winning pumpkin weighed 132 pounds (60 kilograms).

The contest in 2007 set a new world record. The winning pumpkin weighed 1,524 pounds (691 kilograms)! The winner was Thad Starr of Oregon. The grand prize was $6 per pound, for a total of $9,144. "It was definitely worth the trip!" said Mr. Starr.

Thousands of people come to the festival. They admire the many different types of pumpkins. One farmer grew a pumpkin in a bottle. Another farmer grew square pumpkins and painted them to look like dice.

Unit 9

Table of Contents

Kim's Bad Day

Kim had a bad day. Her brother ate the last bowl of Oat-Oh cereal, so Kim had to eat wheat flakes instead.

Then Kim missed the bus. As a result, she was late for school.

Mrs. Lopez gave the class a spelling test. Kim looked at the test and frowned because she had studied the wrong words.

At home, Kim showed her mother the spelling test. Kim's mother knew that Kim was sad, so she gave Kim a big hug. The hug caused Kim to feel loved.

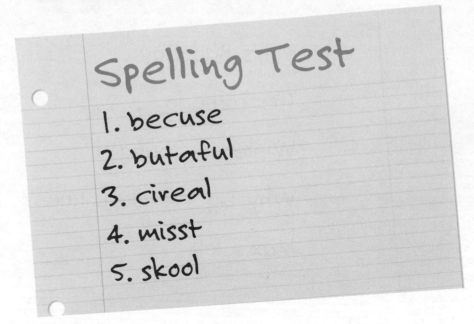

Spelling Test
1. becuse
2. butaful
3. cireal
4. misst
5. skool

Unit 9

The Tornado

The family huddled together in the basement because they were waiting for the tornado to pass. When the roaring finally stopped, they went upstairs. The twister had caused a lot of damage.

The porch was a mess. A window was broken. Garden plants were uprooted and scattered everywhere.

As a result of the tornado, the family had a huge clean-up task ahead of them.

Unit 9

Winter to Spring

The air is usually coldest in winter. The cold air can cause ponds to freeze. To stay warm, people wear jackets, hats, and gloves.

In winter, some animals go underground or into caves to stay warm. Some birds fly to warmer places so they can find food.

Soon we have more sunlight and the days are longer. Because we have more sunlight, we have more heat.

The warmer weather causes snow and ice to melt. We see the birds return because they can find plenty of food now. It's spring!

Why Do We Have Rules?

by Margaret McNamara

Table of Contents

Unit 9

Words to Think About

citizens

These good citizens follow rules about walking.

laws

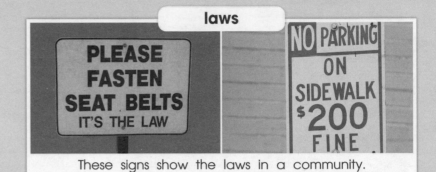

These signs show the laws in a community.

community

People live, work, and play in this community.

rules

Rules help you know what to do.

fairness

You show fairness by waiting your turn.

safe

Wearing a helmet keeps your head safe.

Introduction

Rules are very important. Rules help people understand what they should and shouldn't do.

You follow rules every day. All good **citizens**, or members of a **community**, follow the rules. In this book, you will learn about how rules help people.

▲ You follow rules when you play a sport.

▲ These good citizens follow rules about when to walk.

$1000 FINE FOR LITTERING

▲ People who throw trash on the ground can get in trouble.

Unit 9

Rules That Keep Us Safe

When you get in a car, you put on your seat belt. You know that wearing your seat belt can keep you **safe**.

Wearing a seat belt is also a rule. Your community made this rule to keep you safe.

▲ These signs help people stay safe.

Unit 9

The rules your community makes are **laws**. If you don't follow the laws, you can get in trouble.

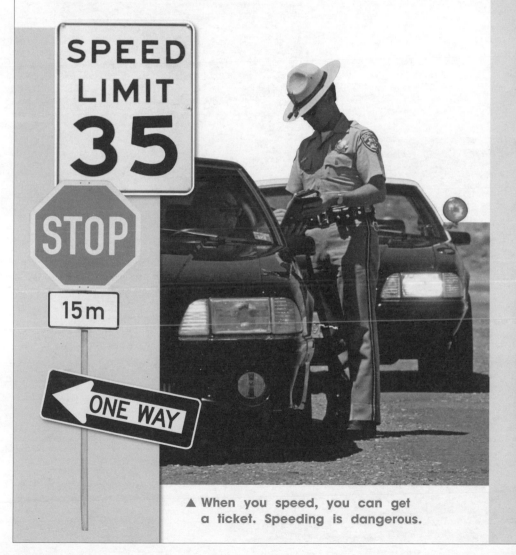

▲ When you speed, you can get a ticket. Speeding is dangerous.

Who Makes Rules?

- Parents make rules at home. Sometimes children help their parents make rules.

- The principal and teachers make rules at school. Sometimes students help their teachers make rules.

- People in state government make rules for the state. Citizens help make the rules, too.

Rules for Fair Play

Everybody wants to be treated with **fairness**. Some rules keep people from treating others unfairly. The rules make sure that everybody gets the same chances.

LOOK AT TEXT STRUCTURE

Description

The author uses the word "fairness" to describe how people like to be treated. What other words does the author use to describe things?

You are being a good citizen when you play by the rules.

▲ When teams play by the rules, everyone gets a chance to win.

◄ Playing by the rules helps everyone get along.

Unit 9

Rules to Care for Earth

Good citizens help take care of Earth. Rules tell people how to do their part.

Most communities have rules about littering. They have rules about recycling, too. What rules help you take care of the planet?

These good ▶ citizens help take care of Earth.

▲ Many communities have rules about recycling.

Unit 9

Conclusion

Good citizens follow many kinds of rules. There are rules for safety and rules for fairness. Some rules protect our planet.

Many Kinds of Rules

Unit 9

Glossary

citizens people who are part of a community

community a place where people live, work, and play

fairness equal chances

laws rules people in a community must obey

rules ideas about what people must do

safe not getting hurt

Max's Job

Max lived in a place that got lots of snow. Max loved to play in snow! He also loved to shovel snow. All the neighbors hired Max to shovel their snow.

One day, Max looked out the window. No snow! "When will we have snow, Mom?" Max asked. "I can't do my job!"

"You could walk dogs instead of shoveling snow," said Mom.

"No way!" said Max. "I don't need people's dogs pulling me all over the place."

The next day, Max looked out the window—still no snow. "I can't do my job!" Max complained to Dad.

"You could be a paperboy," suggested Dad. "No way!" said Max. "The neighbors like me now. They wouldn't like me much if I accidentally threw their papers through a window!"

Thinking about a window made Max look outside. "Come on . . . SNOW!" he said to the sky. Suddenly, a snowflake floated by the window, then another, then another.

"Yeah!" said Max. "I can do my job again!"

Unit 10

Table of Contents

Elmwood Tree

All summer, the children played under Elmwood Tree. They loved the shade of the leaves. Then one day, a cool wind blew. Elmwood tree was sad. "Summer is over. Soon I will have no leaves. The children will not come and play."

Flapper Bird said, "The children will come back. Wait."

Elmwood looked at the other trees. "They have new colors," said Elmwood.

"You have new colors, too," said Flapper. "I will fly to a warm place. You stay and wait for the children."

The next day, one red leaf fell from Elmwood. Then a yellow leaf fell. Soon there were no leaves left on Elmwood. Then the children returned. They jumped in the crisp leaves.

Kids Make a Difference

The park was not pretty. Litter was everywhere.

Julie talked to her friends. "We can pick up the litter," said Julie. "Then the park will look nice again."

Amy wasn't sure. "We're just kids. Can we clean up a whole park?"

"I think kids can make a difference," said Julie.

Julie and her friends spent the afternoon in the park. They picked up newspapers, wrappers, and cans. The kids put all the trash in bags.

At the end of the day, the friends looked around the park. They were very happy.

Flag Day

Americans celebrate Flag Day on June 14. It was on this day in 1777 that the leaders of the United States decided on a design for America's flag. The flag had 13 stripes. Seven stripes were red and six were white.

The flag had 13 stars on a blue background. The 13 stars and stripes stood for the 13 colonies that became the first states. Later, as the United States grew, a star was added for each new state. Today the United States flag has 50 stars.

Stephanie INVESTIGATES

by Susan Hartley • illustrated by Lisa Blackshear

Stephanie Jones (also known as Stephi) checked the sign again. It looked impressive. Business should come rolling in.

"What do you think, Arch?" she asked.

Archimedes rolled over in the grass and closed his eyes. He had better things to think about.

Stephi sat inside her office and waited ... and waited.

"Hey, Steph!" her friend Nate called. "Come to the park with me."

"Can't. I've got a business to run," Stephi answered.

"Come for a little while. It doesn't look good if you just sit in your office doing nothing."

"Good thinking," Stephi said.
She left a note on her office.
It read, "Out on a case.
Back later." And she took off.

"I'll race you to the lake,"
Stephi said to Nate.

The two set off along the trail.
Suddenly Stephi put on her brakes.

Unit 10

"Look at that bird," Stephi said. "It's got some icky stuff on its wings. I think it might be oil."

"Let's take it to the wildlife rescue," said Nate.

They carefully wrapped the bird in Stephi's jacket and rode off.

"Yes, it has oil on its wings," said the woman at the wildlife rescue center. "Motorboats often spill oil into the water. The oil gets on the birds."

Unit 10

"We can probably save this bird. We have to wash it in detergent several times. Then we'll make sure we've rinsed off all the soap. If we don't, the bird won't be able to float."

"Nate," said Stephi. "We've got a mystery on our hands. How did oil get on the bird's wings? Motorboats aren't allowed on this lake. Someone must be breaking the law. We'll have a stakeout and catch the culprit."

Unit 10

Nate and Stephi got ready for the stakeout. First, they packed binoculars and a camera. Then they packed some snacks and books and took off.

Nate and Stephi waited in the bushes for more than an hour, but nothing suspicious happened.

They ate all the food they had brought. Stephi took some pictures around the lake. But still nothing suspicious happened.

Unit 10

"We've been here forever. We haven't seen anything except that truck parked by the lake," complained Nate. "You can do the stakeout on your own tomorrow."

The next day, Stephi saw the truck again. She used her binoculars to get a closer look. A man was putting a big barrel into the lake. "That's funny," she thought. She took a picture.

Unit 10

That afternoon Stephi went to the garage with her mom. She watched a man do an oil change. "What do you do with the oil?" she asked him.

"We put it in those barrels, then a truck takes the barrels away."

Stephi had the answer to her mystery! "Would that truck belong to Jim's Disposals?" she asked.

"Yes," the man said.

At home, Stephi looked at the photos she had taken. One of them showed a man rolling a barrel into the water.

"That's it!" Stephi exclaimed. "He's putting barrels of oil into the lake. That must be how the bird got oil on its wings."

Stephi went to the police station with her mom.

"You're a very good detective," the policewoman said. "That guy probably didn't want to pay the disposal fees. It's lucky you found out before he could do too much damage to our lake."

The next day, Stephi was at her office with Arch and Nate. She had a new sign.

Stephanie Investigates
EXPERIENCED

What Is This Story About?

Use the pictures below to retell the story and tell what pictures belong in the empty spots.

start here

What happens here?

What happens here?

finish here

Pockets

I love my old blue overalls,
my favorite thing to wear.

I carry all my special things
inside my pockets there.

In one I have a piece of chalk
to draw a four-square line.

One pocket holds some raisins,
a favorite snack of mine.

One pocket holds a long, red string
I use to spin my top.

In one I carry my pet frog
'til he jumps out . . . *KERPLOP!*

Two pockets hold my favorite books—
I love to sit and read.

I carry all my special things,
and always have what I need.